Little Larry

Lyrics by David Sparks
Illustrated by Cesar E. De Castro
Painted by Kathy W. Kim
Designed by Barry K. Haun

© 2001 Little Star Entertainment
  West Covina, California 91791

Published by the Character Building Company
West Covina, California 91791
www.characterbuilding.com
Printed in Korea
ISBN 1-931454-01-9

Library of Congress cataloging-in-publication data is available from the publisher.

Songs in this book are from the **Character Classics** series and are available on cassette and CD. **Coming soon the video series.**

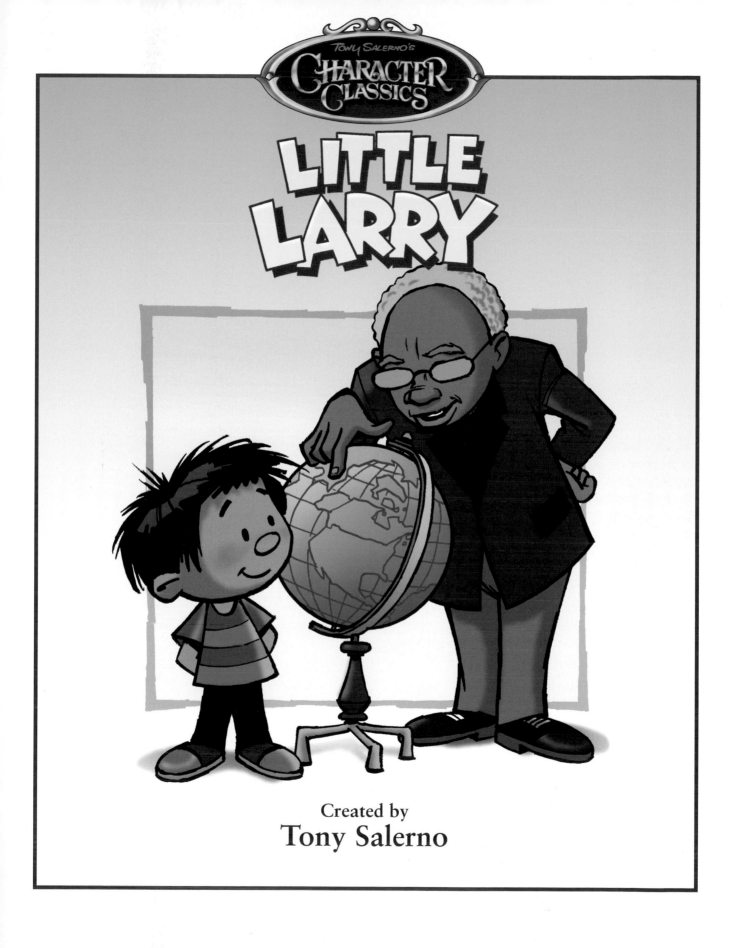

Little Larry

Orpheus in the Underworld/Allegretto Movement - Jacques Offenbach

Can can can you pay attention,
Do I have to mention
All the times you didn't listen,
Can you hear me?
Can can can you pay attention,
Do I have to mention,
Everything I said, I'll say again!

Can can can you pay attention,
Do I have to mention
All the times you didn't listen,
Can you hear me?
Can can can you pay attention,
Do I have to mention,
Everything I said, I'll say again!

Little Larry never listened to a word his mother said,
She said walk and Larry ran, he never seemed to understand and
When she told him follow me, he'd turn and walk the other way,
Stop was go and go was stay,
I think I heard his mother say-

Can you hear me?
Listening is good for you,
Pay attention,
Maybe you'll learn something new,
Little Larry,
What am I to do with you,
Larry, Larry,
Everything you put me through!

Can can can you pay attention,
Do I have to mention
All the times you didn't listen,
Can you hear me?
Can can can you pay attention,
Do I have to mention,
Everything I said, I'll say again!

Larry's mother's in the kitchen baking up blueberry pies,
She said leave the pies alone, but Larry couldn't figure why so
Larry ate the whole thing up and now he's turned completely blue,
Always listen to your mom, she knows a little more than you!

Can you hear me?
Listening is good for you,
Pay attention,
Maybe you'll learn something new,
Little Larry,
Oh, what am I to do with you,
Larry, Larry,
Now you've turned completely blue!

Can can can you pay attention,
Do I have to mention
All the times you didn't listen,
Can you hear me?
Can can can you pay attention,
Do I have to mention,
Everything I said, I'll say again!

Can can can you pay attention,
Do I have to mention
All the times you didn't listen,
Can you hear me?
Can can can you pay attention,
Do I have to mention,
Everything I said, I'll say again!
The things I said, I'll say again!

Now picture this song as you read or sing along...

Can can can you pay attention,
Do I have to mention
All the times you didn't listen,
Can you hear me?

Can can can you pay attention,
Do I have to mention
All the times you didn't listen,
Can you hear me?

Can can can you pay attention,
Do I have to mention,
Everything I said,
I'll say again!

Little Larry never
listened to
a word his
mother said,
She said walk and
Larry ran,
he never seemed
to understand and

When she told him follow me,
he'd turn and walk the other way,
Stop was go
and go was stay,
I think I heard
his mother say-

Can you hear me?
Listening is good for you,

Pay attention,
Maybe you'll learn something new,

Little Larry,
What am I to do with you,
Larry, Larry,
Everything you put me through!

Can can can you pay attention,
Do I have to mention
All the times
you didn't listen,

Can you hear me?

Can can can you pay attention,
Do I have to mention,
Everything I said, I'll say again!

Larry's mother's in the kitchen
baking up blueberry pies,
She said leave the pies alone,
but Larry couldn't figure why so

Larry ate the whole thing up
and now he's turned completely blue,
Always listen to your mom,
she knows a little more than you!

Can you hear me?
Listening is good for you,

Pay attention,
Maybe you'll learn something new,

Little Larry,
Oh, what am I to do with you,

Larry, Larry,
Now you've turned completely blue!

Can can can you pay attention,
Do I have to mention
All the times you didn't listen,

Can you hear me?

Can can can you pay attention,
Do I have to mention,
Everything I said, I'll say again!

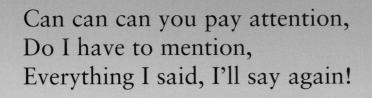

Can can can you pay attention,
Do I have to mention
All the times you didn't listen,

Can you hear me?

Can can can you pay attention,
Do I have to mention,
Everything I said,
I'll say again!

The things I said, I'll say again!

Find a Friend

The Nutcracker Suite - Waltz of the Flowers
Peter Tchaikovsky

Sarah was rather sad
She had no one now to play with
She had just moved into a new town
And her friends were nowhere to be found
Starting a new school with lots of boys
And girls and teachers with new faces!

Sarah felt all alone
No one to talk to, to laugh with
She wanted to hide and not be found
She kept her eyes turned down to the ground
This was such a scary day to start school!
No one to be near her,
No one saw her shed a tear!

But suddenly a smiling face approached her
        (someone had seen her)
Standing in the corner
        (now they would greet her)
"Welcome to our school now
        (my name is Brandon)
Would you be my friend today?

"I saw you standing all alone with sad eyes
        (no one to talk to)
So I thought that I would
        (come and be with you)
I know what it's like to
        (be in a new school)
'Cause I'm new myself!
It's my first day, too!"

Look around you,
Find someone new
Go ahead and share a kind word
Find a new friend,
Give a smile then,
This is how making friends begins.

Look around you,
Find someone new
Go ahead and share a kind word
Find a new friend,
Give a smile then,

When you see someone sad
Sad, with nobody to talk with
Greet them with a warm and friendly smile
Wear a grin that's wider than a mile.
Pay attention to the needs of others,
Spread a ray of sunshine
Happiness is what you'll find.

Look around you,
Find someone new
Go ahead and share a kind word
Find a new friend,
Give a smile then,
Pay attention to others' needs.

Watch and Listen

Symphony No. 94, Second Movement - Surprise Symphony
Franz Joseph Haydn

Never stand behind a mule,
Take a crocodile to school,
Never bathe an elephant unless you have a pool.
Never swat an angry bee,
Chase a monkey up a tree,
Never sit beside a skunk, no one will sit by you! Phew!

Watch and listen,
You can learn a lesson and some good advice,
So watch and listen all day long,
Pay attention and you can't go wrong.

Watch and listen,
You can learn a lesson and some good advice,
So watch and listen all day long,
Pay attention and you can't go wrong.

Don't disturb a sleeping bear,
Ride an ostrich if you dare,
Never swim with hungry sharks or dinner could be you! OOO!
Never grab a tiger's tail,
Try to catch a killer whale,
Never pet a porcupine, surely you'll get poked! Ouch!

Watch and listen,
You can learn a lesson and some good advice,
So watch and listen all day long,
Pay attention and you can't go wrong.

Watch and listen,
You can learn a lesson and some good advice,
So watch and listen all day long,
Pay attention and you can't go wrong.

Pay Attention

Symphony No. 9, 4th Movement - Ode to Joy
Ludwig van Beethoven

Pay attention, listen, children,
Hear the words I share today.
They'll keep you safe in times of troubles
Listen well, and then obey.

Treat each other with love and kindness,
Always do right, and turn from wrong.
Take my words and pay attention,
Hear the message of this song!

Listen to your moms and dads,
For words of wisdom they impart.
They'll teach you how to treat each other
And to love with all your heart.

Listen, children, listen closely,
Mom and Dad know what to do.
They'll guide you if you'll only listen,
They know what is best for you.

Treat each other with love and kindness,
Always do right, and turn from wrong.
Take my words and pay attention,
Hear the message of this song!

Listen, children, to your teachers
As they guide you while at school.
Do your homework, read your lessons,
Always keep the golden rule!

In the classroom,
While on the playground,
Help one another and be kind!
Keep these words and soon discover
You will have a brilliant mind!

Treat each other with love and kindness,
Always do right, and turn from wrong.
Take my words and pay attention,
Hear the message of this song!
Take my words and pay attention,
Hear the message of this song!

Goat on a Boat

Radetzky March
Johann Strauss I

Here's a tale you can tell if you listen well,
'Bout a boat that's afloat on a castle moat,
And aboard that boat there's a Billy goat in a grey overcoat, did I mention?
In the coat on the goat, is a one-page note,
For the goat has a note that his mother wrote,
And upon that note, she wrote
All the following that I will quote!

What I bring to the king is a diamond ring,
And the ring that I bring is for marrying,
My son to your daughter,
Crossed over the water, long he has sought her,
Your lovely daughter,
Oh, King, take the ring that I gladly bring,
And all of the people will dance and will shout and will sing!

What I bring to the king is a diamond ring,
And the ring that I bring is for marrying,
My son to your daughter,
Crossed over the water, long he has sought her,
Your lovely daughter,
Oh, King, take the ring that I gladly bring,
And all of the people will dance and will shout and will sing!

Well, he looked at the goat in the overcoat,
In a boat set afloat on a castle moat,
And he held that note Billy's mother wrote,
And the king cleared his throat, and he said,

I'm afraid, I must say, that the goat can't stay
So the king told the goat he should sail away,
And the reason why he did,
Little Billy Goat was just a kid!

Now you've heard every word and the tale's complete,
Every word that you've heard, you can now repeat,
Hope you listened through, 'cause it's up to you,
Do the very best that you can do!

What he brings to the king is a diamond ring,
And the ring that he brings is for marrying,
Her son to the king's daughter,
Crossed over the water, long he has sought her,
The king's lovely daughter,
Oh, King, take the ring that he gladly brings,
And all of the people will dance
and will shout and will sing!

Now you've heard every word and the tale's complete,
Every word that you've heard, you can now repeat,
Hope you listened through, 'cause it's up to you,
Do the very best that you can do!

Fine.

fee´·nay
A musical term for the end.